ما أروع الطعام

Food, Food, Fabulous Food

Written by Kate Clynes

Illustrated by MW

Re-telling in Arabic by Abdelhalim Zeid

MANTRA LINGUA

Food, food, fabulous food,
It gives us our energy and makes us feel good,
Poke it and break it, nibble it and shake it,
There's nothing quite like it, fabulous food.

أيها الطعام، كم أنت رائع،
تمنحني الراحة حين أكون جائع،
وتمدني بالطاقة حين أتناولك،
لا شيء يشبه الطعام الرائع.

أيها الطعام، كم أنت مذهل،
تجمع الأحباب، فنسعد ونأمل،
مهما اختلفت أشكالك وألوانك،
لا شيء يشبه الطعام المذهل.

Food, food, wonderful food,
It brings us together, which always feels good,
Share it and pick it, poke it and lick it,
There's nothing quite like it, wonderful food.

Food, food, beautiful food,
It builds up our muscles to work as they should,
Grab it and tear it, hold it and share it,
There's nothing quite like it, beautiful food.

أيها الطعام، كم أنت جميل،
تقوّي عضلاتنا، فنفعل المستحيل،
مهما اختلف قوامك ومذاقك،
لا شيء يشبه الطعام الجميل.

Food, food, shopping for food,
What shall we ask for it all looks so good,
See it and buy it, pack it and try it,
There's nothing quite like it, choosing our food.

هيا بنا لنشتري طعامنا،
ماذا سنختار؟ هذا قرارنا،
نشتري الطعام ونجربه في البيت،
لا شيء يشبه اختيارنا لطعامنا.

Food, food, making our food,
Follow the recipe, cook something good,
Mix it and shake it, cook it and bake it,
There's nothing quite like it, making our food.

هيا بنا لنُعد طعامنا،
نتبع الوصفة، ونطهوه بأنفسنا،
نمزجه ونقلّبه، ونخبزه بأيدينا،
لا شيء يشبه إعداد طعامنا.

Food, food, growing our food,
Out in the sunshine, we all feel so good,
Plant it and water it, love it and talk to it,
There's nothing quite like it, growing our food.

هيا بنا لنزرع طعامنا،
في نور الشمس، والسعادة تغمرنا،
نزرعه ونسقيه، ونمنحه حبنا،
لا شيء يشبه زراعة طعامنا.

Food, food, incredible food,
It puts us all in a very good mood,
Beautiful colours, and various shapes,
Nature's amazing, just look what it makes.

ما ألذّك أيها الطعام،
تمنحنا الغذاء ونشعر بالسلام،
ما أجمل ألوانك وأشكالك،
ما أروع الطبيعة وجمالها الأخّاذ.

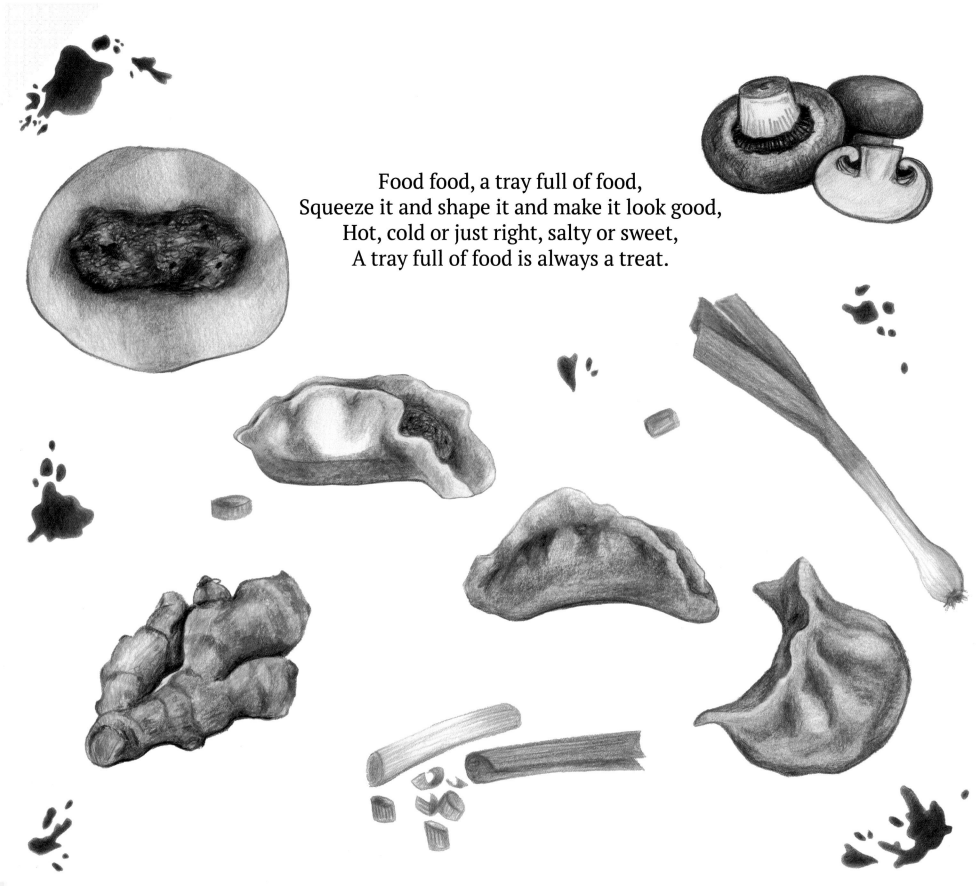

Food food, a tray full of food,
Squeeze it and shape it and make it look good,
Hot, cold or just right, salty or sweet,
A tray full of food is always a treat.

أنواع الطعام تُشعرني بالسعادة،
أُنهي صحني، وأطلب الزيادة،
ساخن أو بارد، حلو أو حارّ،
تنويع الطعام هو أجمل عادة.

Drink, drink, fill up our cup,
Milk, juice or water, right up to the top,
Pour it or tip it, splash it or drip it,
Carefully does it, to not spill a drop.

دعونا لا ننسى المشروبات اللذيذة،
حليب أو عصير، أو المياه المفيدة،
نشربها على اختلاف أشكالها،
ولا نهدرها، لأنها عزيزة.

Food, food, healthy food,
Our tummies are rumbling, it all smells so good,
See it and serve it, as we all deserve it,
There's nothing quite like it, waiting for food.

ما ألذّ الطعام الصحي،
يثير شهيتي، إنه المفضّل لديّ،
أنتظر الطعام حتى ينضج،
وأقدمه لجميع أحبائي.

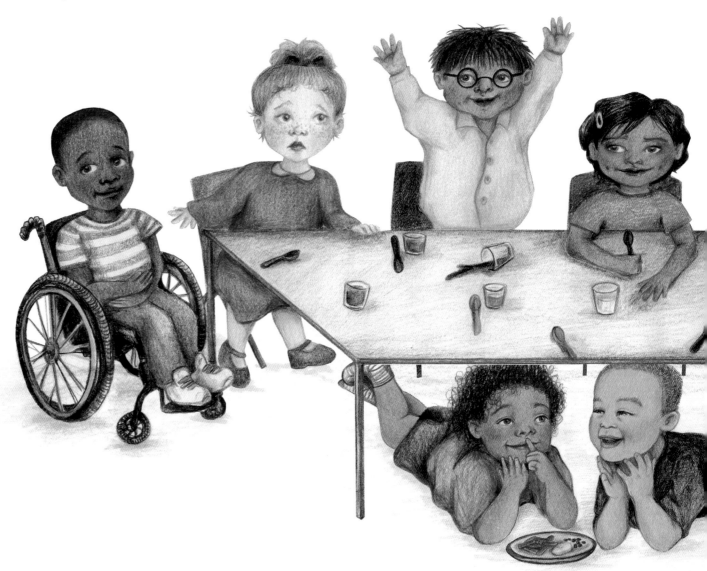

Food food sharing our food,
So many choices and all of them good,
We all love each other and we all agree,
There's nothing quite like it, to keep us healthy.

كم أحب مشاركة الطعام،
إنه متنوع ولذيذ، يا سلام!
اتفقت أنا وجميع أحبائي
أن الطعام وسيلتنا، لنظل بأفضل حال.

For Ellis and Indigo and Nora and Ruby
– KC

For Edie and Otis
– MW

Hot Peppers, Ginger, Jerk Spices, Paprika, Saffron, Basil, Hibiscus, Oregano, Cumin

Parsley, Celery, Mint, Dill, Curry Powder, Cardamom, Ginger, Cinnamon, Nutmeg, Mustard

Fresh Chilies, Coriander, Cumin, Cinnamon, Oregano, Cloves, Allspice, Thyme, Epazote

Saffron, Harissa, Dukkah, Cinnamon, Mint, Cumin, Sumac, Parsley, Coriander, Lakama, Ras El Hanout

Cinnamon, Dill, Ginger, Juniper Berries, Nutmeg, Allspice, Savory Cloves, Paprika, Black Pepper

West Indies United Kingdom South America North Africa Eastern Europe

First published in 2019 by Mantra Lingua
Global House, 303 Ballards Lane, London N12 8NP
www.mantralingua.com

Text copyright © 2019 Kate Clynes
Illustration, audio and dual language copyright © 2019 Mantra Lingua

This sound-enabled edition published 2021.

ISBN 978-1-78784-312-7
Printed in UK